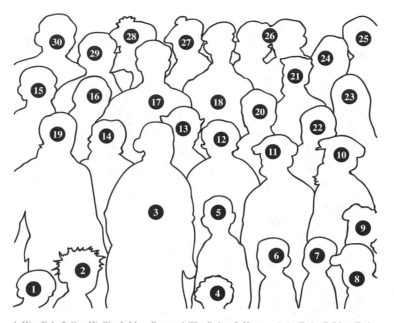

1. Wee Eck, 2. Oor Wullie, 3. Maw Broon, 4. The Bairn, 5. Horace, 6. Ae Twin, 7. Ither Twin, 8. Boab, 9. Soapy, 10. Granpaw Broon, 11. Paw Broon, 12. Daphne Broon, 13. Jimmy Shand, 14. Robert Louis Stevenson, 15. Morris Heggie, 16. Sir Alex Ferguson, 17. Andy Murray, 18. Hen Broon, 19. Rabbie Burns, 20. John Logie Baird, 21. Joe Broon, 22. Sir Walter Scott, 23. Maggie Broon, 24. Amy Macdonald, 25. Sydney Devine, 26. The Proclaimers, 27. Sir Harry Lauder, 28. Nessie, 29. Andy Stewart, 30. Sir Kenny Dalglish.

Great Scots

The Broons

With their long history beginning in 1936, The Broons have well established themselves as Scottish icons. They're Scotland's happiest and most famous family, but they're not the only great Scots to have appeared in the pages of The Sunday Post. From Granpaw's tall tales of the Broons' ancestor who aided Robert the Bruce, to Maw dressing up as Mary Queen of Scots, there are famous folk and Scots aplenty to be seen in this collection from DC Thomson's archives!

Oor Wullie

He's oor Wullie, your Wullie and a'body's Wullie! From his tackety boots to his dungarees, the wee scunner is Scottish to the bone! So popular is the cheeky chappy that many famous faces have popped by to Auchenshoogle to say hello – and Wullie himself is good pals with folks like Amy MacDonald, Ewan McGregor, and Andy Murray!

© DCT Consumer Products (UK) Ltd 2019
D.C. Thomson and Co. Ltd,
185 Fleet Street,
London EC4A 2HS

Printed in the EU

It's no' until the very end,

That Wullie kens just who's his friend!

Braw Bards

Wordsmiths like Rabbie Burns, William Shakespeare and William Wordsworth have featured in The Broons and Oor Wullie many a time. But don't forget another famous William – Wullie himself! He and Horace Broon are both pretty nifty with a poem or two!

The crocus, snowdrop and the lily
Are inspiration to Oor Willie!

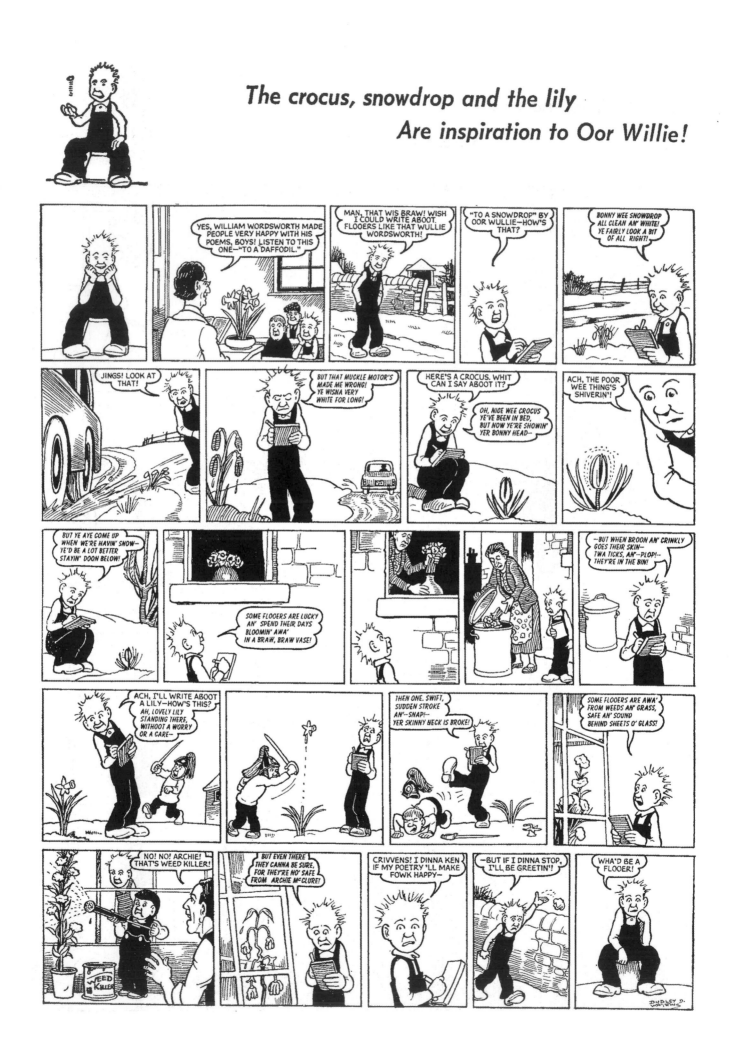

Wouldn't ye know it?

The Broons ken this poet.

Here's a famous Scottish pair —

Oor Wullie and the Bard of Ayr.

A lot o' folk get big surprises —

When Wullie finds some wig disguises.

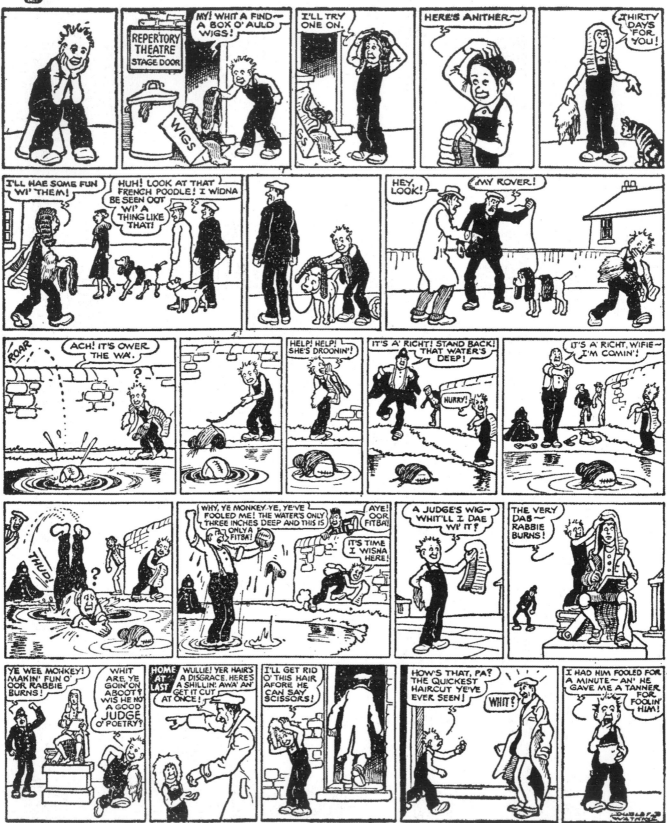

HEN AN' JOE ARE IN A FLUSTER

LOOKIN' AT THE AULDEST HUSTLER!

Michty me! It surely looks like Wullie's really intae books!

Paw reckons it's jist no' fair —

— when fowk poke fun at his lack o' hair.

That angry fist comes thumpin' doon—
Then things look black for puir Paw Broon!

Who'd have thocht? They're awfy slick . . .

. . . when it comes tae arithmetic!

It's role playin' time for you-know-who —
He's a detective without a clue.

Elementary! Although not many would peg Wullie as a bookworm, the wee boy loves a good story. Here he is emulating the famous character Sherlock Holmes created by Sir Arthur Conan Doyle, who was born in Edinburgh.

The missing pie's a real whodunnit —

and someone has to eat their bunnet!

Wullie plays at Robinson Crusoe,
But never again "Wull-ie" do so!

Have ye ever heard o' Big Black Broon?—

He fairly got the Redcoats doon!

Scot Free | Family history is important to The Broons, who can trace their ancestors back through Scottish history all the way to the Jacobites and beyond – according to Granpaw's tall tales about Big Black Broon that is!

Gran'paw would never let ye doon—
wi' the history o' Big Black Broon!

"ANYWAY, WEE BLACK BROON DIDNA FORGET THIS AND, ABOUT TEN YEARS LATER WHEN HE WAS BIG BLACK BROON, HE WIS WAITIN' WITH HIS BROTHERS HENRY AN' JOCK WHEN THAE REDCOATS CAME BACK UP TO KILLIECRANKIE FOR THEIR HOLIDAYS—"

"—AND AS QUICK AS LIGHTNIN', THE THREE BROONS GRABBED THE REDCOATS' HOLIDAY MONEY TO PAY FOR THE HAGGIS THEY STOLE A' THAE YEARS BACK, AN' WERE OFF ACROSS THE MOORS LIKE THE WIND, WITH THE REDCOATS HOT ON THEIR HEELS—"

"—BIG BLACK BROON AN' HIS BROTHERS HID IN SOME BUSHES AN' THE ENGLISH SOJERS COULDNA FIND THEM ANYWHERE! THAT'S WHEN THE BROON LADS HAD A BRAW IDEA—"

"—THE THREE O' THEM LEAPED OUT AND JABBED THEIR CLAYMORES INTO THE REDCOATS—AND, JINGS, DID THEY JUMP !! WHY THEY JUMPED RIGHT OVER TO THE OTHER SIDE O' THE RIVER—"

Wullie doesn't like this joke one bit—

Because he FEELS the point of it!

See this swordsman's greatest feat —

He wins the day — in full retreat !

Fat Bob, the swordsman, is beaten here—

Outsmarted by a MOUSEketeer!

Maybe now he'll hold his tongue—

About the Family bein' stung!

The Broons men have always done their part for King (or Queen) and country, first fighting in World War One, then again in World War Two, depending on when the strip was written.

Wi' shield and claymore aff they go—

A' set for battle wi' the foe!

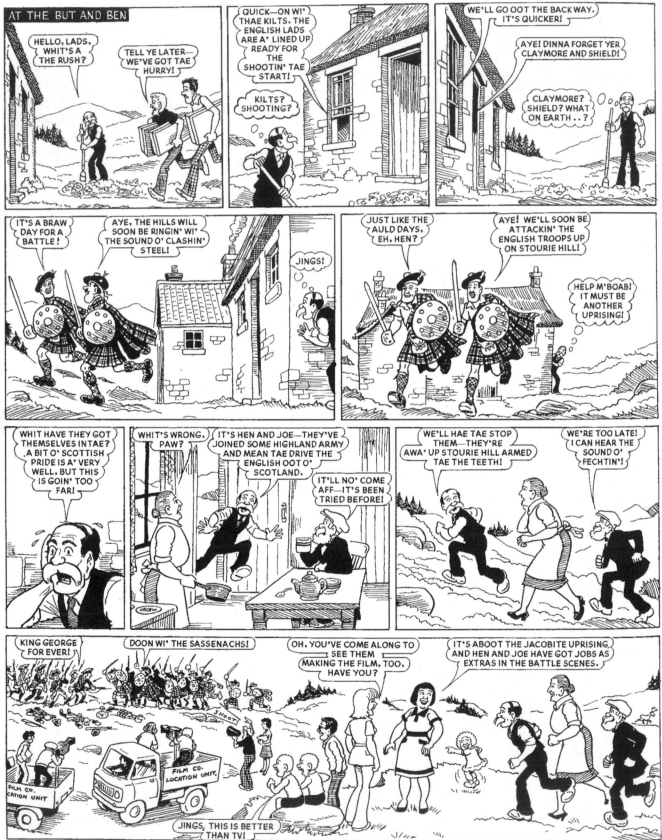

WHA'S AULDEST IN THE BIG PARADE?

GRANPAW THINKS HE'S GOT IT MADE!

Surely gallant knights of old—

Didn't have to do as Wullie's told!

Where and when was the Broon clan founded?—

Gran'paw's tale will leave ye astounded!

Help m'Boab, here's a funny sight —

You'll laugh a' day at this wee knight!

Time doesn't seem to change their luck

Once more, the Broons are fairly stuck

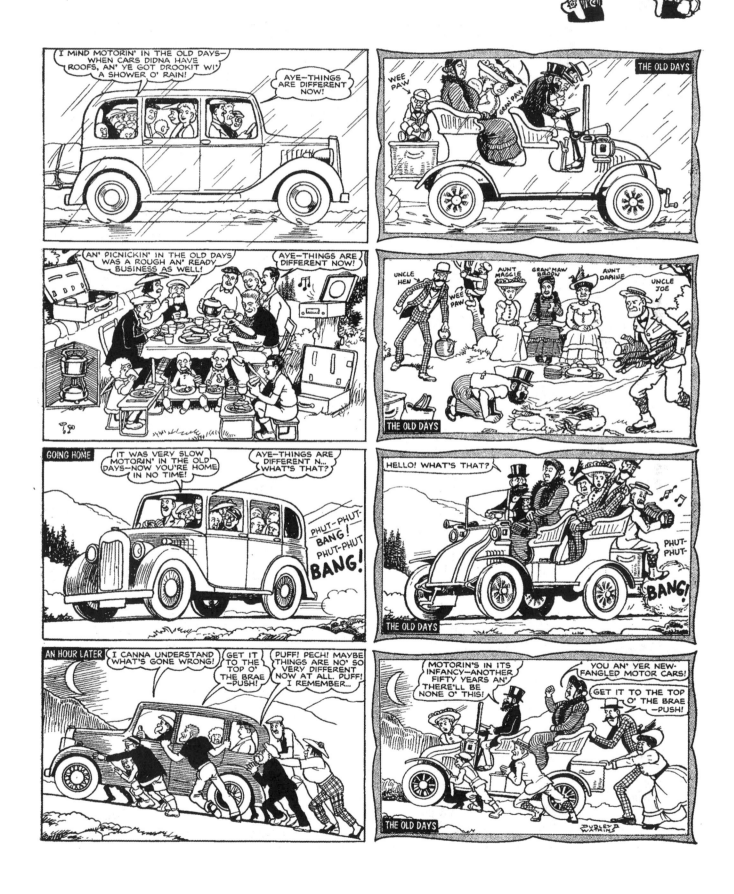

Blackbeard Wullie comes to grief —

As a bold, bad pirate chief.

The deeds of this hero—

All add up to—ZERO!

Long hair's a handy thing, by gosh—

It means ye've no' so much to wash!

See how all the Broons got drookit—

They feel real fools—and they sure look it!

Wullie's tale of bygone days . . .

. . . earns him teacher's highest praise!

That English lad's ta'en down a peg—

When Wullie starts to pull his leg!

Heads or tails? What d'you say—

That's the way it's done today!

Wullie's filled with consternation—

It seems he's no imagination!

It costs the visitor four pound —

When Wullie shows him around!

Wullie gets his licks, puir craitur —

For tryin' tae be a " personator."

The household's in confusion when —

Hen and Joe join up again!

Paw Broon finds it never 'pays'—

To brag aboot the Good Old Days!

When it comes to making noise—

You must admit, MEN will be boys!

It's no' as Hen and Joe had feared—

There's more than ONE Broon wi' a beard!

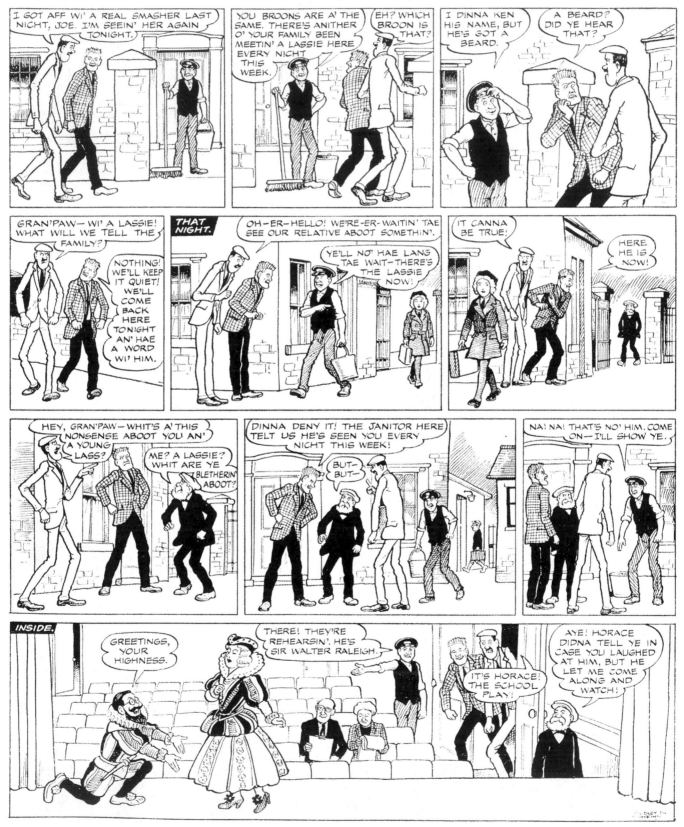

A spaced-oot suit –
just isnae cute.

Rugby's in his plans just now,

but Wull mis-kicks the ball and how!

Paw's got the family in a tizz —

It seems he's in a telly quiz!

It wasn't long before 'The Munro Show's Muriel Gray joined the ranks of famous Scot cameos in The Broons.

Oor Wullie's capers —

Wi' comic papers.

Jeemy does just as he pleases . . .

slippers, bed an' lots o' cheeses!

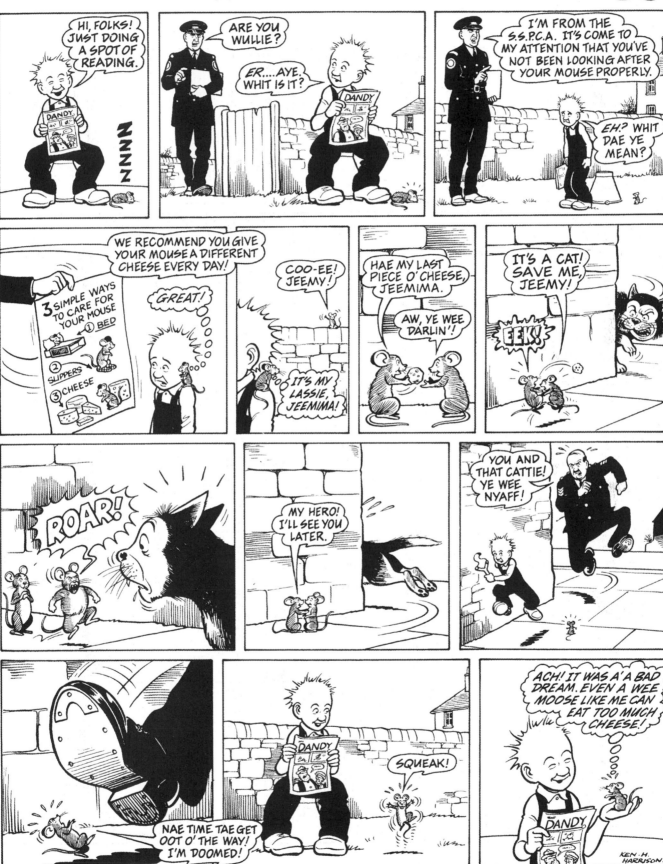

He's worried efter what he's read.

What's goin' on in Wullie's head?

It really is, without a doubt,

the bedroom of a litter lout!

What's this about history and 1066? —

Oor Wull prefers comics — and then gets his flicks.

Here's some laughs—

With shadowgraphs!

It's lucky teacher didn't look—

Inside Oor Wullie's great big book!

Wull's uncle's only four feet twa —

But, in a fecht, he's really braw!

It's NOT the music, truth to tell,

That has wee Jeemy under a spell!

Address tae a Haggis

With strips including everything from kilts to ceilidhs, bagpipes to bairns, porridge to puddocks, and haggis to Hogmanay, you can take The Broons and Wullie out of Scotland but you can't take Scotland out of them.

Years ago, same time, same place—

Paw Broon had the same red face!

Tossing the caber, putting the shot —
When Wullie tries, it's a laughalot!

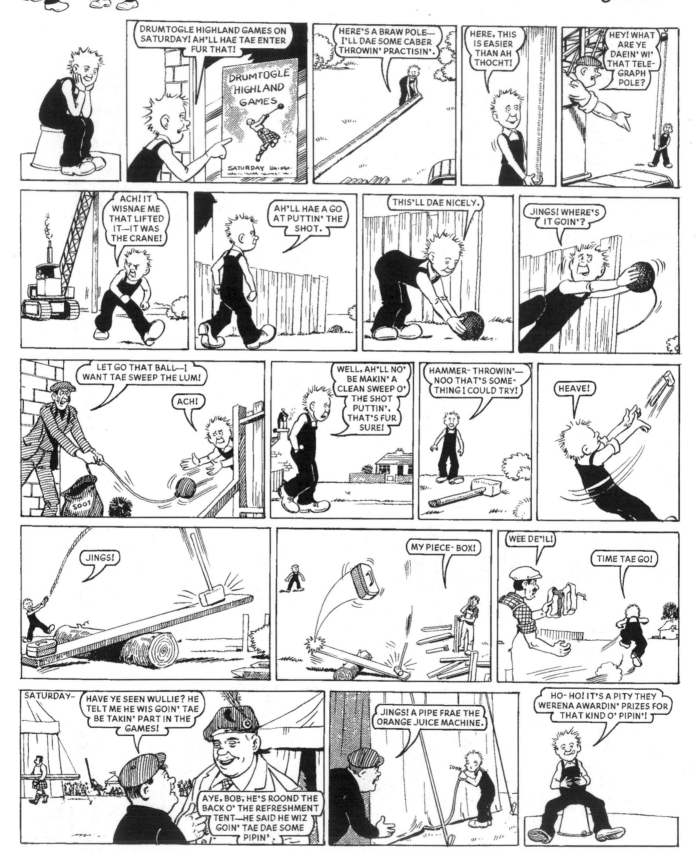

Like its neighbour, Auchentogle, you don't have to look far in Auchenshoogle for a Highland fling, as the residents rarely miss a chance to shake their bahoochies in their favourite tartans!

When it's time tae celebrate New Year—

This " shortie " tak's the biscuit here!

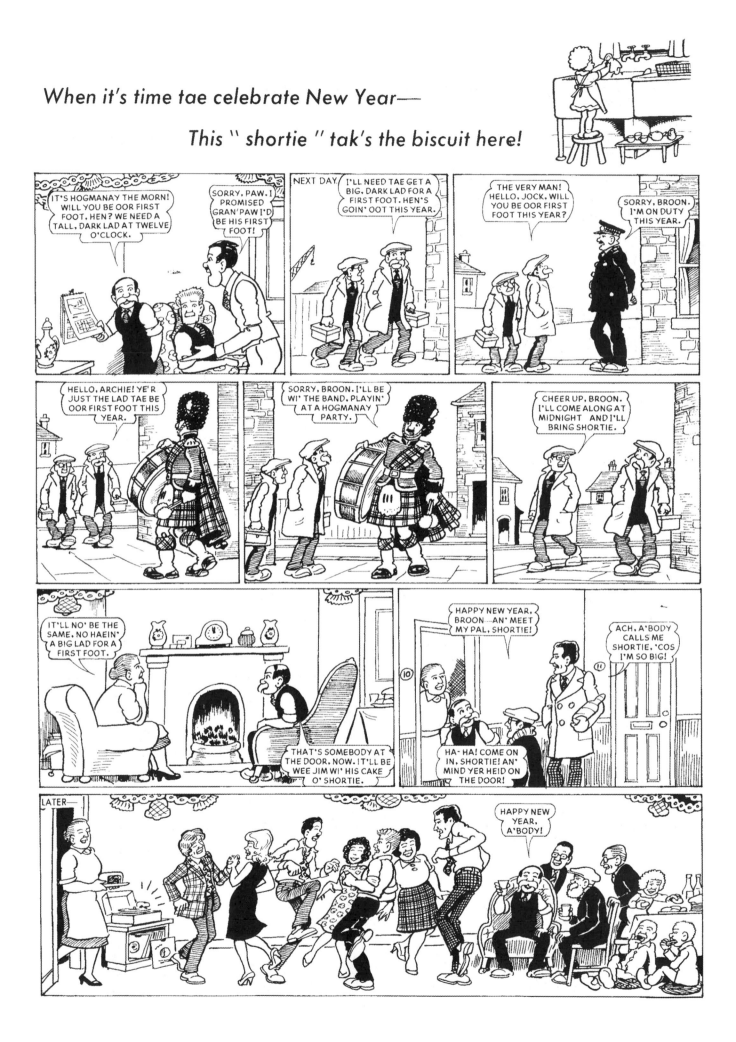

A yacht becalmed? See Wullie's wheeze—

He quickly conjures up a breeze!

Kilted an' wi' sword in hand —

The tartan terror o' the land!

Their fitba' kit's a proper shocker.

They need a deal tae lift their soccer!

Daphne's holiday date—

Sounds great, but wait!

Here's a laugh! Stand by for—

The great Glensporran tug-o'-war!

Burns' Nicht the Broons all wish—

Tae sample Scotland's "national dish"!

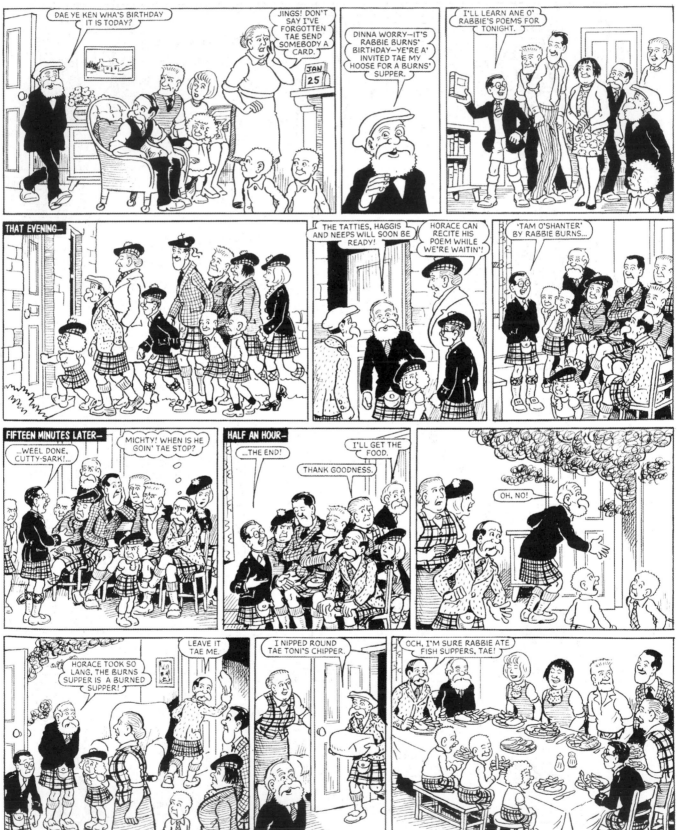

Eatin', shootin', makin' merry —

Jings, it's great tae be a Terrie.

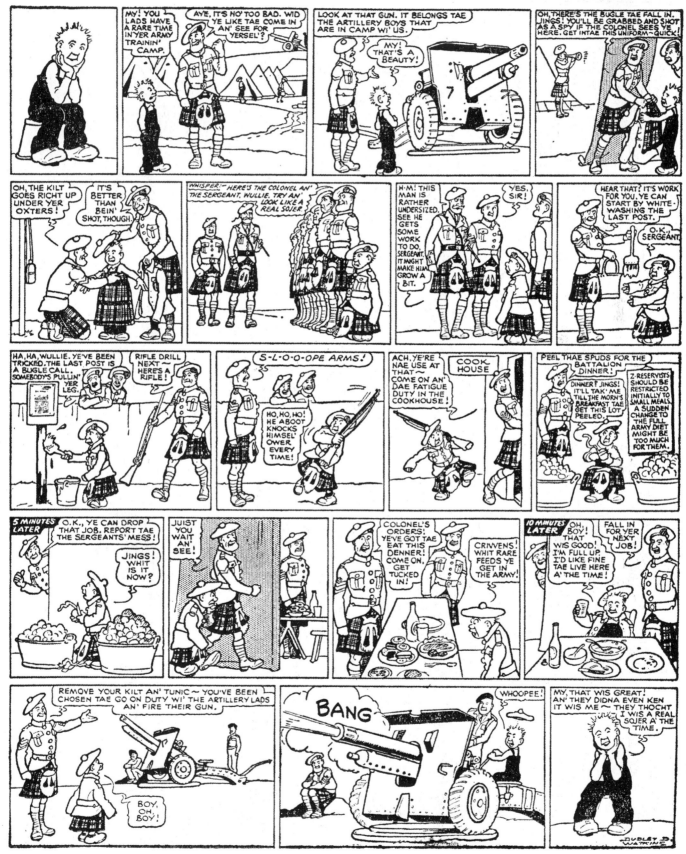

IT'S NAE WONDER FOWK ARE STARING.

LOOK AT WHAT THEY'RE WEARING!

Paw's not pleased, he's filled with ire —

— at Granpaw's reunion dinner attire.

Over the past eighty years, debates have often raged over where Auchentogle might be in Scotland, however this strip offers one answer as the Army regiment the Black Watch was made up of recruits primarily from Fife, Angus, Perth and Kinross, and Dundee — where DC Thomson's head office is based!

Wullie's no' that hard to please —

A' he wants is dungarees!

Murdoch's sure a funny mannie,

lookin' mair like Jessie-Annie!

Beggars can't be choosers—

When you're on the hunt for troosers!

Ma didnae laugh —

— at Wull's school photograph!

Oh, what a hoot—

With this 'Royal Salute'!

The Broons all get a real let-down—

When Lord Lavelock comes to town!

Here's a CORDIAL invitation—

To a New Year celebration!

A'body looks just like a rabbit —

— nae wonder Wullie's feelin' wabbit!

Oban, Killin, the Bonnie Braes —

Were all alike to Paw Broon's gaze.

While the people are the bedrock of Scotland, there's much to be said for its iconic monuments. From Edinburgh Castle to the Tay Bridge, these landmarks as are just as recognisable a part of Scotland in The Broons and Oor Wullie.

Oor lad's a Scot, we can't deny it—

He's even on a haggis diet!

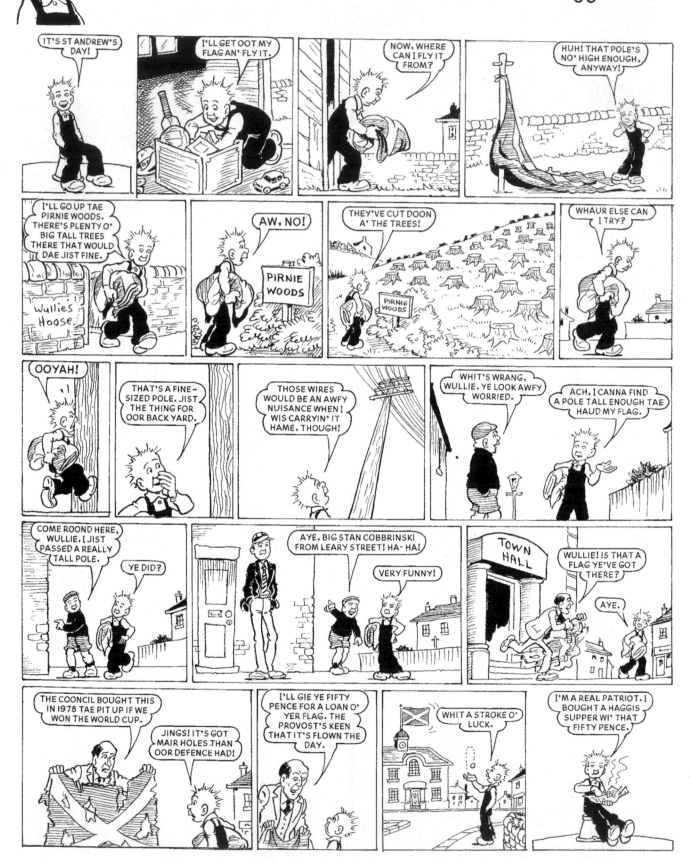

Celebrating the patron saint of Scotland, Saint Andrew's Day is an official flag day in Scotland, and Wullie is always keen to be seen waving the Saltire!

Hurlin' haggis, he loses traction,

settin' aff a chain reaction!

His chums mair Scottish? Don't be silly —

they're no' a PATCH on fly Oor Wullie!

This new lad's nae catch . . .

for their fitba' match!

Twa Beanos let you see Wull's slides—

And get a load o' laughs besides!

Wullie near sinks to his knees,

seein' wha's in dungarees!

Wi' a hundred blaws an' a' and a' —

Oor Wullie scares the craws awa'!

Wullie thinks he's on a winner —

huntin' for the family dinner!

Hiram from the U.S.A.—

Meets his match in Wull today!

Myths and Legends

Scotland's lore is rich and plentiful, filled with gothic castles, ghostly apparitions, and who could forget the nation's most beloved monster — oor Nessie!

Hen and Joe get a fright—

From a very ` fishy ` sight!

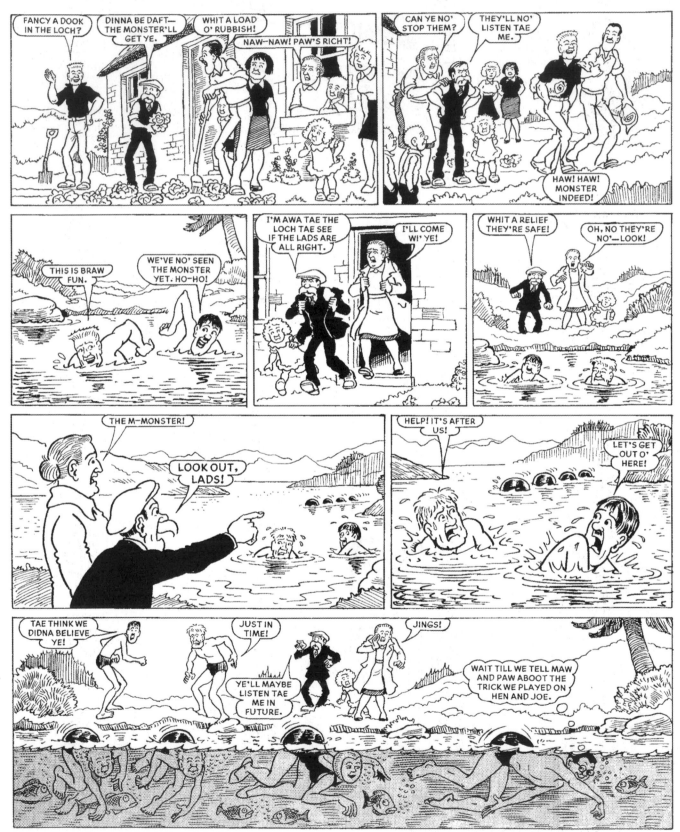

Look at Wull! He canna wait

tae eat his tasty monster bait!

Stand by for shocks—

At the castle stocks!

What would life be withoot a care?

Wull wants tae be a millionaire!

Wullie's in an awfy mess —

Ridin' on his steed, Black Bess!

As well as spooky myths, Oor Wullie has also had a go at dressing up as other legends from pirates to knights and other heroes he's always keen to play the master of disguise!

Sir Wull helps maidens in distress.

He wins one's hand. But where? Just guess!

The Laughing Pirate sails the seas,
In tacketty boots and dungarees!

Wullie as a ' Pirate '—why?—

There's more to this than meets the eye!

Michty me, ye'll never guess —

Whit Wullie is in fancy dress!

Take a look! Withoot a doot—

Here's a proper thorn-proof suit!

See 'St. George', on his wee cuddy—

He fairly tickles everybody!

Paw's a canny kind o' fella —

His special first foot — Cinderella!

It's a total pantomime . . .

. . . when it comes tae Hen's show-time!

It's not just famous Scots the Broons and Oor Wullie love to pay homage to,
as classic pantomimes often feature close to Christmas.

Wullie thinks he's spoiled the scene—

But a better laugh there's never 'bean'!

A staple shown in both 1995 and 1966, the story of Jack and the Beanstalk is always a delight, especially with Wullie as the disobedient son and poor Hen as the lanky green shoot.

Imagine Wullie as a star—

With flashy suit and great big car!

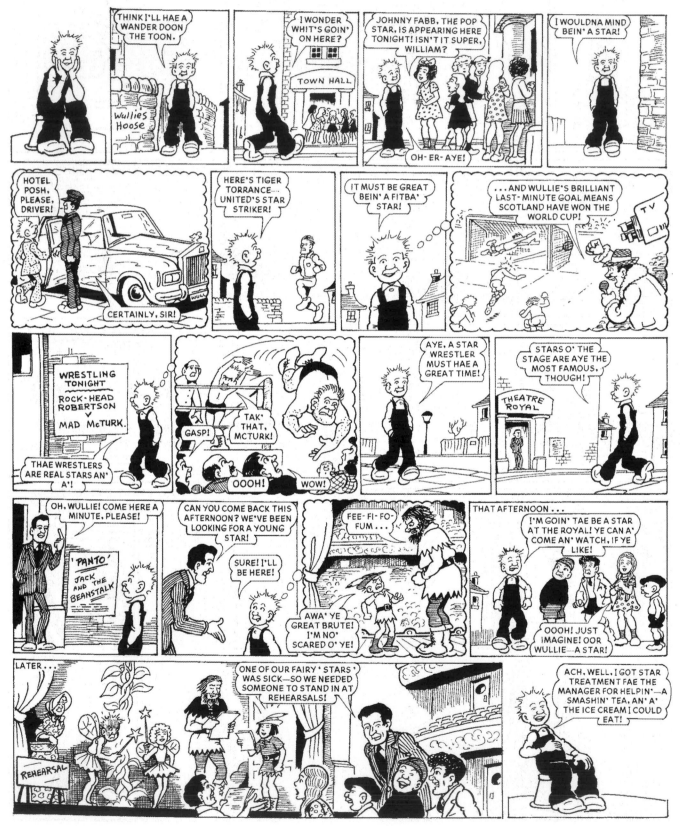

The things that people have tae dae —

When they're actin' in a play!

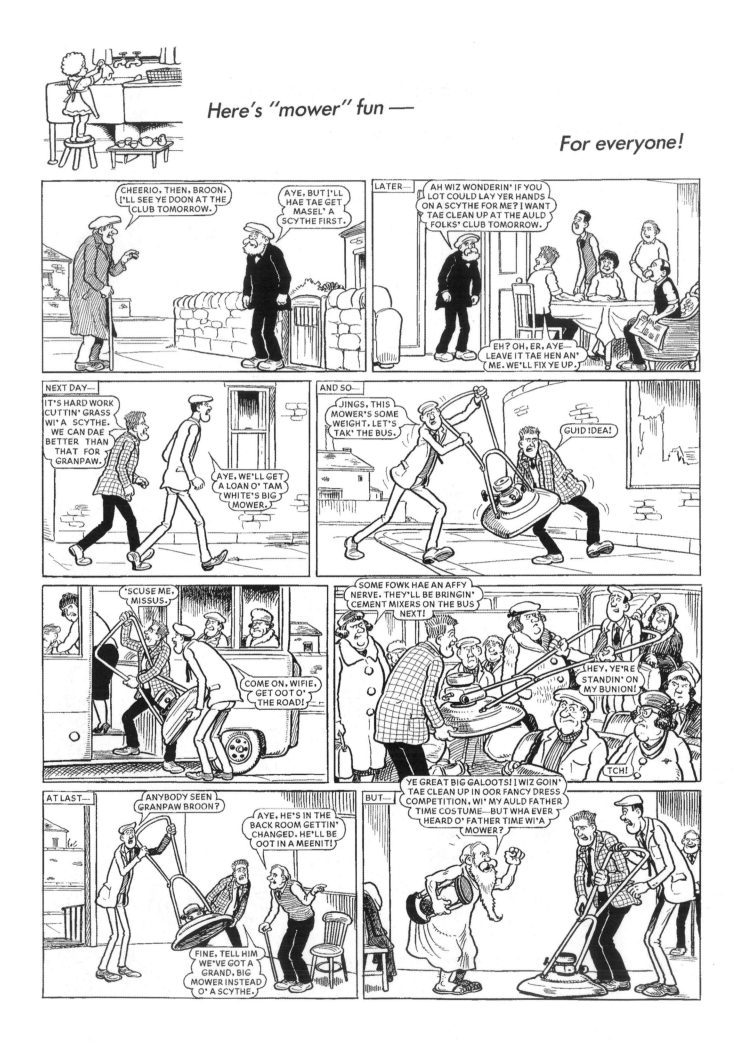

There's something fishy going on here—

When the lassies' posters disappear!

Silver Screen Sirens | The Broons and Oor Wullie never miss a trip to the pictures to see their favourite stars. Ever the eye for a hunk, Rock Handsome, a play on '60s heartthrob Rock Hudson, is often romanced over by Maggie and Daphne.

"Heads or tails?" says Joe. "I'll toss!"

But that idea's a real dead 'loss'!

Maw and Paw get peace, today—

By GOING with the family!

There's just one snag aboot a tacket—

It doesn't half set up a racket!

Auld-time picters are the best—

for giving Paw Broon's tongue a rest!

Wull does his best to guard that box—

But in the end, it gives him shocks.

Paw Broon's found . . .

an answer tae the sound!

Gran'paw Broon does his stuff—

The champion at Blind Man's Buff!

Wild West or Romance? What's it to be?—

Here's a case of WAIT then SEE!

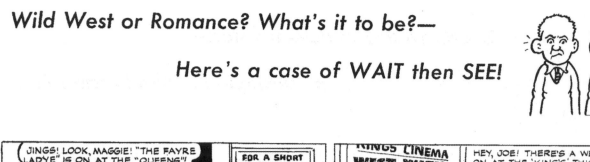

The sad tale o' a pie—

And a big black eye!

Paw says faintly, " Send for a bobby —

There's fower bogles in our lobby!"

Music

From folk to pop, Scotland's sounds range greatly, tuning in to varying genres of music throughout the years. No matter the occasion, there's always a song in our Scottish heroes' hearts.

. . . but there's one special tune —

That's liked by EVERY Broon!

The family hae a big to-do —

— when Daphne says she wants a tattoo.

Wullie's one-man-band —

is really something grand!

You'll all agree—just ask the Broons—

There's nothing like the old Scots tunes!

Capercaillies are a' very well,

but chicken's better, truth tae tell!

Jings, it's true! What a to-do!

The Bairn knows her onions too!

From Harry Lauder to The Police, artist Ken H. Harrison featured many national and
international music stars in his strips.

Modern music micht be tops —

but ye canna whack "Top of the Cops"!

Drumsticks, swords and cricket wicket—
Wull thinks this rock is just the ticket!

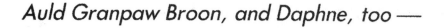

Auld Granpaw Broon, and Daphne, too —

Dinna half shake you-know-who!

Oor Great Scots!

Special guest appearances in The Broons and Oor Wullie aren't just relegated to historical figures and celebrities: great Scots in their own right, characters from the two strips often cross-over, visiting their Sunday Post neighbours.

Wullie's no' a great success —
Carryin' on in fancy dress.

Paw Broon goggles when he sees—

His daughters in their dungarees!

When picking apples, Wullie's clever—

He's got the deepest pockets ever!

There's a scamp on P.C. Wullie's 'beat'—

The oldest 'bairn' you'll ever meet!

Wull doesn't stop till Gran'paw's caught—

Aye, this ploy really 'caps' the lot!

Hip hooray — for Hogmanay! —

an' efter it comes New Year's Day!

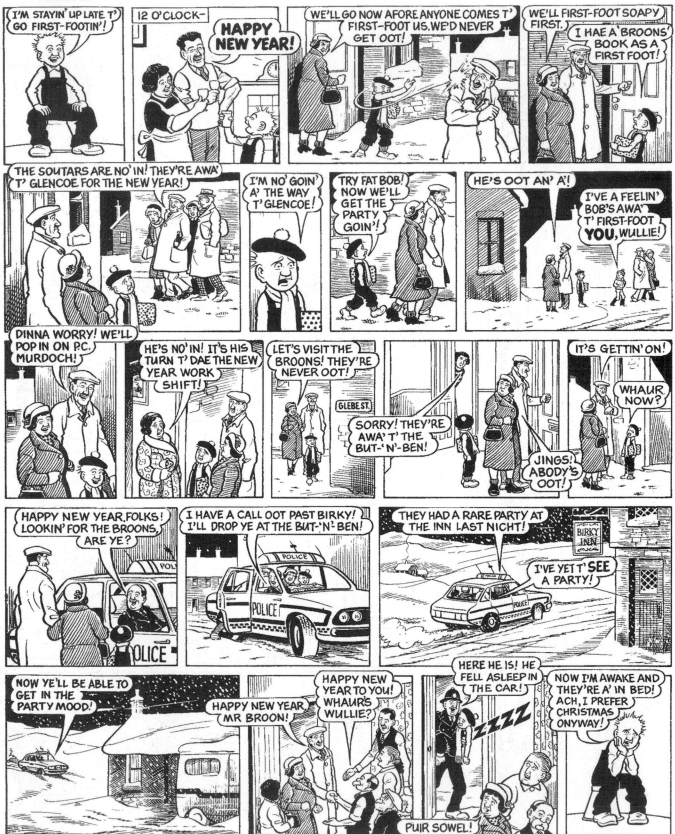

THEY THINK THE BAIRN'S A RICHT WEE GEM —
SHE'S GOT TICKETS FOR THE GEMME!

Maist Famous Folk!

Having been around for over eighty years, The Broons and Oor Wullie have often achieved their own level of celebrity, garnering attention on television and in the press.

Poet Wullie's doing fine —

He gets a laugh wi' every line.

It's nae use lookin' —

— for Maw's home cookin'!

He'd like a photie o' some note,

but Bob gets ain that gets his goat!

The King o' Scotland's first job —

— knight Sir Soapy, Eck an' Bob!

There you have it: The Broons have reached their celebrity status and
Wullie has claimed his bequeathed place as Scotland's newest king – even if only for one day!

Great Scots and Other Famous Folk

Although much has changed in the past eighty years, some icons remain the same and will always be remembered. Scotland's history, landscape and talent is vast, commemorated in numerous strips from The Broons and Oor Wullie's immense archive.

Because of the delight they bring, a welcome and recognisable sight in many a home, we hope you agree that The Broons and Oor Wullie are each just as famous and as great a Scot as many of those who share the pages with them.